The National Songbook 2

Novello & Company would like to thank all who have helped with this songbook.
Particular thanks go to Lucy Kehoe and class 3S0 at Balgowan Primary School, Beckenham for the cover illustration and
Heather Sargeant (Learning and Language Support Teacher, Surrey County Council) for help in compiling the songs.

www.musicroom.com/
thenationalsongbook
Download pdfs of all song lyrics from
this website by entering the code
FT931

NOVELLO PUBLISHING LIMITED
part of The Music Sales Group
London/New York/Paris/Sydney/Copenhagen/Berlin/Madrid/Tokyo

1. A-Roving 4

2. The Ash Grove 6

3. The Animals Went In
Two By Two 8

4. The Bare Necessities 9

5. The Best Day Ever 12

6. Do-Re-Mi 14

7. The British Grenadiers 16

8. Don't Dilly Dally (My Old Man) 17

9. Erev Shel Shoshanim 20

10. Food, Glorious Food 22

11. Froggy Went A-Courting 24

12. God Is So Good 25

13. The Harp That Once
Through Tara's Halls 26

14. He's Got The Whole
World In His Hands 27

15. High Hopes 28

16. I Have A Dream 30

17. I Believe I Can Fly 32

18. I Know An Old Lady
Who Swallowed A Fly 34

19. It Takes A Hundred Years 36

20. Jerusalem 38

21. Hum, Hum! 40

22. Kookaburra Sits In
The Old Gum Tree 41

23. King Without A Thing 42

24. Land Of My Fathers 44

25. Lean On Me 46

26. London Bridge 47

27. My Grandfather's Clock 48

28. Nellie The Elephant 50

29. Please Mr Organ-Man 53

30. On Ilkley Moor Baht 'At 54

31. Oranges And Lemons 56

32. Reach 58

33. Raindrops Keep Fallin'
On My Head 60

34. Right Said Fred 62

35. Shout For Happiness 64

36. Show Me The Way
To Go Home 66

37. The Sun Has Got
His Hat On 68

38. The Salley Gardens 70

39. Scarborough Fair 71

40. The Skye Boat Song 72

41. Sur Le Pont d'Avignon 73

42. Three Little Fishes 74

43. Top Of The World 76

44. When You Believe 78

45. Who's Been Polishing
The Sun 80

46. With A Little Help
From My Friends 82

47. Ye Banks And Braes 84

48. You Are My Sunshine 86

49. This Beautiful Day 88

50. Edward Lear's Round 91

1. A-Roving

Traditional

LYRICS

At number three Old England Square,
Mark well what I do say;
At number three Old England Square,
My Nancy Dawson she lived there,
And I'll go no more a-roving with you, fair maid!

A-roving, a-roving
Since roving's been my ru-i-in
I'll go no more a-roving with you, fair maid!

My Nancy Dawson, she lived there,
Mark well what I do say;
She was a lass surpassing fair
With bright blue eyes and golden hair,
And I'll go no more a-roving with you, fair maid!

A-roving, a-roving…

I met her first when home from sea,
Mark well what I do say;
Home from the coast of Africee
With pockets lined with gold monee,
And I'll go no more a-roving with you, fair maid!

A-roving, a-roving…

Oh, didn't I tell her stories true,
Mark well what I do say;
And didn't I tell her whoppers too
Of gold we found in Timbuctoo,
And I'll go no more a-roving with you, fair maid!

A-roving, a-roving…

But when she'd run my money through,
Mark well what I do say;
And all the gold from Timbuctoo –
She cut her stick and vanished too!
So I'll go no more a-roving with you, fair maid!

A-roving, a-roving
Since roving's been my ru-i-in
I'll go no more a-roving with you, fair maid!

Steady tempo

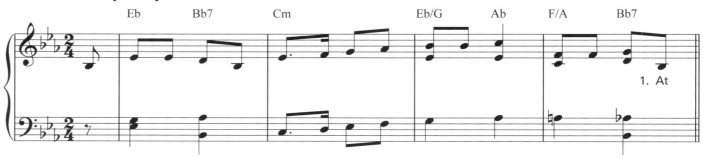

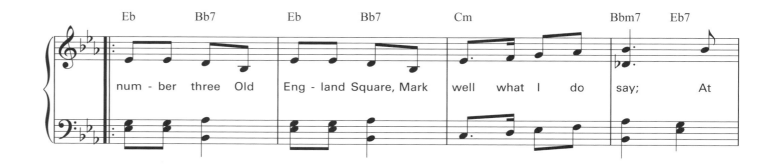

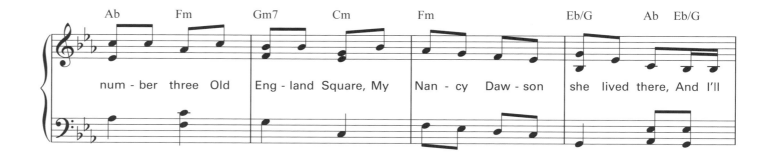

4

ABOUT THE SONG

A-roving is a sea shanty, which is a song that would have been sung by sailors. Apart from being a nice thing to do to pass time, the singing of shanties also helped facilitate a rhythm whilst working, so repetitive tasks were carried out with consistency and rigour.

ACTIVITIES

Find more sea shanties!

LYRICS

Down yonder green valley
   where streamlets meander,
When twilight is fading, I pensively rove;
Or at the bright noontide in solitude wander,
Amid the dark shades of the lonely Ash Grove.
'Twas there while the blackbird
   was cheerfully singing,
I first met that dear one, the joy of my heart!
Around us for gladness the bluebells were ringing;
Ah! Then little thought I how soon we should part.

Still glows the bright sunshine
   o'er valley and mountain,
Still warbles the blackbird its note from the tree;
Still trembles the moonbeam
   on streamlet and fountain,
But what are the beauties of nature to me?
With sorrow, deep sorrow, my bosom is laden,
All day I go mourning in search of my love;
Ye echoes! Oh tell me, where is the sweet maiden?
"She sleeps 'neath the green turf
   down by the Ash Grove."

2. The Ash Grove

Traditional

Flowing tempo

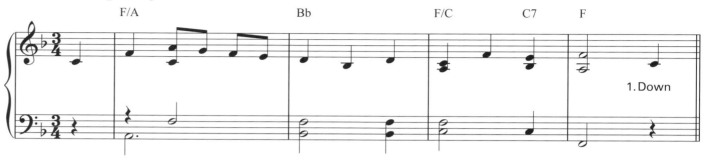

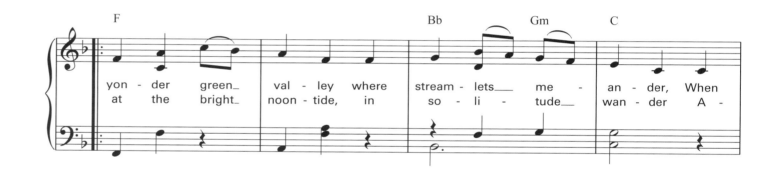

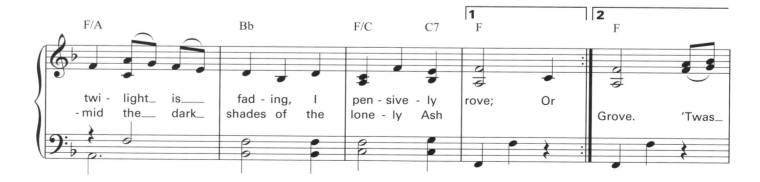

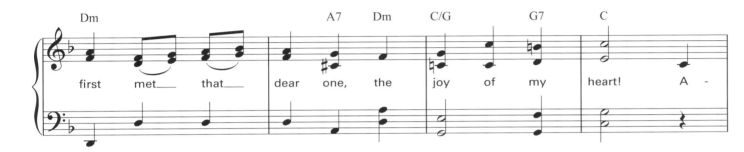

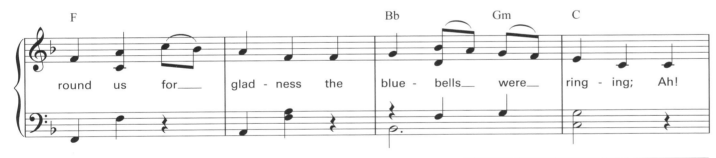

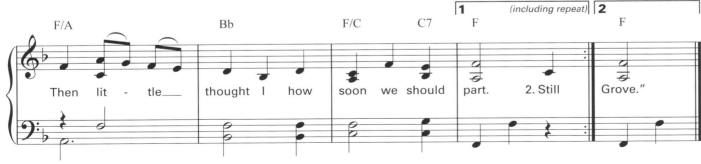

WELSH MUSIC

This is a Welsh folk song. Wales has a long history of folk music, particularly singing. It is famous for its male voice choirs, some of which are known worldwide.

Like England, Wales also has many brass bands, mostly former colliery bands from the time when mining was still a major industry.

WELSH FACTS

Wales is one of the four countries that make up Great Britain. Wales is not represented on the British flag. Wales is home to the town with the longest name in the world, which is Llanfairpwllg-wyngyllgogerychwyrndrobwllllantysiliogogogoch.

MAKE WELSH CAKES

These are very easy to make, and taste really good.

You will need:
225g/8oz self-raising flour
110g/4oz butter
85g/3oz caster sugar
1 egg
sultanas

Sieve the flour into a bowl with the sugar. Rub in the butter to make small crumbs. Add the egg and a handful of sultanas and mix it all together. If it's a bit dry then add a tiny bit of milk to make a light dough.

Roll out the dough so it is about 0.5cm thick and cut into circles (about 5-10 cm diameter) so they are disc-shaped.

Heat a pan and spread some butter thinly over it. Cook the welsh cakes for 2-5 minutes on each side – until they are golden brown.

Sprinkle some more sugar over when warm, and eat either warm or at room temperature.

LYRICS

The animals went in two by two, hurrah! Hurrah!
The animals went in two by two, hurrah! Hurrah!
The animals went in two by two,
The elephant and the kangaroo,
And they all went into the Ark,
For to get out of the rain.

The animals went in three by three, hurrah! Hurrah!
The animals went in three by three, hurrah! Hurrah!
The animals went in three by three,
The wasp, the ant and the bumble bee,
And they all went into the ark,
For to get out of the rain.

The animals went in four by four, hurrah! Hurrah!
The animals went in four by four, hurrah! Hurrah!
The animals went in four by four,
The great hippopotamus stuck in the door,
And they all went into the ark,
For to get out of the rain.

The animals went in five by five, hurrah! Hurrah!
The animals went in five by five, hurrah! Hurrah!
The animals went in five by five,
They warmed each other to keep alive,
And they all went into the ark,
For to get out of the rain.

The animals went in six by six, hurrah! Hurrah!
The animals went in six by six, hurrah! Hurrah!
The animals went in six by six,
They turned out the monkey because of his tricks,
And they all went into the ark,
For to get out of the rain.

The animals went in seven by seven, hurrah! Hurrah!
The animals went in seven by seven, hurrah! Hurrah!
The animals went in seven by seven,
The little pig thought he was going to heaven,
And they all went into the ark,
For to get out of the rain.

3. The Animals Went In Two By Two

Traditional

March tempo

4. The Bare Necessities

Composed by Terry Gilkyson

LYRICS

Look for the bare necessities,
The simple bare necessities;
Forget about your worries and your strife.
I mean the bare necessities,
Old Mother Nature's recipes
That bring the bare necessities of life.

Wherever I wander, wherever I roam,
I couldn't be fonder of my big home.
The bees are buzzin' in the trees
To make some honey just for me.
When you look under the rocks and plants
And take a glance at the fancy ants,
Then maybe try a few.
The bare necessities of life will come to you,
They'll come to you.

Look for the bare necessities,
The simple bare necessities;
Forget about your worries and your strife.
I mean the bare necessities,
That's why a bear can rest at ease
With just the bare necessities of life.

When you pick a paw-paw or a prickly pear
And you prick a raw paw, well next time beware.
Don't pick the prickly pear by the paw;
When you pick a pear, try to use the claw.
But you don't need to use the claw
When you pick a pear of the big paw-paw.
Have I given you a clue?
The bare necessities of life will come to you,
They'll come to you.

LYRICS

Mister Sun came up and he smiled at me.
Said it's gonna be a good one, just wait and see.
Jumped out of bed, and I ran outside,
Feeling so extra ecstatified.

It's the best day ever.
It's the best day ever.

I'm so busy, got nothing to do,
Spent the last two hours just tying my shoe.
Ev'ry flow'r, ev'ry grain of sand
Is reaching out to shake my hand.

It's the best day ever.
It's the best day ever.

Those clouds don't scare me, they can't disguise
This magic that is happ'ning right before my eyes.
Soon Mister Moon will be shining bright,
So the best day ever can last all night.

It's the best day ever. Now!

5. The Best Day Ever
(from 'The SpongeBob SquarePants Movie')

Composed by Tom Kenny & Andy Paley

Final time to Coda ⊕

This song is from the popular American animated TV series *Spongebob SquarePants*.

SpongeBob wakes up with a great day planned, thinking it will be The Best Day Ever. It begins badly when SpongeBob can't go to work at The Krusty Krab restaurant due to an infestation, so SpongeBob helps to get rid of it. He then visits his friend Sandy, to do Karate, but there's a leak in Sandy's roof so Karate is cancelled. SpongeBob fixes the leak with his Karate glove! He then goes to meet his friend Patrick to fish together, but Patrick has broken his net. SpongeBob lends Patrick his new net even though he is left without one. Lastly SpongeBob goes to his friend's clarinet recital but is not let in because he has no ticket. They eventually let him in when they find his name on the guest list, but by then the recital has ended. When SpongeBob's friends see that he is unhappy they put on another show especially for him, for helping them all so much. Here SpongeBob sings *The Best Day Ever*.

ACTIVITIES

Write about your best day ever, and why it was the best.
Is 'ecstatified' a word?
See Edward Lear's Round (page 91) and read about nonsense words.

LYRICS

Doe, a deer, a female deer,
Ray, a drop of golden sun,
Me, a name I call myself,
Far, a long long way to run.
Sew, a needle pulling thread,
La, a note to follow sew,
Tea, a drink with jam and bread,
That will bring us back to do, oh, oh, oh!

Doe, a deer, a female deer,
Ray, a drop of golden sun,
Me, a name I call myself,
Far, a long long way to run.
Sew, a needle pulling thread,
La, a note to follow sew,
Tea, a drink with jam and bread,
That will bring us back to Do!
Do-re-mi-fa-so-la-ti-do!

6. Do-Re-Mi
(from 'The Sound Of Music')

Words by Oscar Hammerstein II
Music by Richard Rodgers

Bright, with a bounce

ABOUT THE SONG

From the 1959 musical *The Sound Of Music*, the lead character Maria uses this song to teach the Von Trapp children how to sing.

'Do Re Mi' are the first three notes of a major scale when using the Solfège system. This system gives every note a name – Do, Re, Mi, Fa, So, La, Ti.

ACTIVITIES

Teach children the whole scale first, singing each note with the correct Solfège name, accompanying on the piano if possible.

LYRICS

Some talk of Alexander and some of Hercules;
Of Hector and Lysander,
   and such great names as these;
But of all the world's brave heroes,
   there's none that can compare,
With a tow, row, row, row, row, row, row,
   to the British Grenadiers.

None of those ancient heroes
   e'er saw a cannonball,
Or knew the force of powder,
   to slay their foes withal;
But our brave boys do know it,
   and banish all their fears,
Singing tow, row, row, row, row, row, row,
   to the British Grenadiers.

Then let us fill a bumper,
   and drink a health to those
Who carry caps and pouches,
   and wear the looped clothes;
May these and their commanders
   live happy all their years,
With a tow, row, row, row, row, row, row,
   to the British Grenadiers.

ABOUT THE SONG

An old marching song, *The British Grenadiers*
is famously played at Trooping the Colour outside
Buckingham Palace in June each year. A
'Grenadier' was originally a soldier employed
specifically to throw grenades at the enemy. As
grenades became less important, the Grenadiers
remained a strong and important army unit.

PERCUSSION

Try playing the following rhythm on drums:

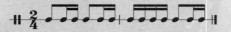

7. The British Grenadiers

Traditional

8. Don't Dilly Dally (My Old Man)

Words & Music by Fred W. Leigh & Charles Collins

© Copyright 2009 Novello & Company.
All Rights Reserved. International Copyright Secured.

LYRICS

We had to move away,
 'cause the rent we couldn't pay.
The moving van came round just after dark:
There was me and my old man,
 shoving things inside the van,
Which we'd often done before, let me remark.
We packed all that could be packed
 in the van, and that's a fact:
And we got inside all we could get inside,
Then we packed all we could pack
 on the tailboard at the back,
Till there wasn't any room for me to ride.

My old man said, "Follow the van,
Don't dilly dally on the way!"
Off went the cart with the home packed in it,
I walked behind with my old cock linnet.
But I dillied and dallied, dallied and dillied,
Lost the van and don't know where to roam.
I stopped on the way to have the old half quartern,
And I can't find my way home.

I gave a helping hand
 with the marble wash-hand stand,
And straight, we wasn't getting on so bad.
All at once the carman bloke
 had an accident and broke,
Well, the nicest bit of china that we had.
You'll understand of course,
 I was cross about the loss,
Same as any other human woman would.
But I soon got over that,
 what with "two-out" and a chat
'Cos it's little things like that what does you good.

My old man said, "Follow the van...

Oh! I'm in such a mess, I don't know the new address.
Don't even know the blessèd neighbourhood;
And I feel as if I might have to stay out all the night
And that ain't a-goin' to do me any good.
I don't make no complaint, but I'm coming over faint,
What I want now is a good substantial feed.
And I sort o' kind o' feel, if I don't soon have a meal
I shall have to rob the linnet of his seed.

My old man said, "Follow the van...

19

Words by Moshe Dor
Music by Josef Hadar

LYRICS

Erev shel shoshanim,
Netze na el habustan,
Mor besamim ulevona,
Leraglech miftan.

Shachar homa yonah,
Roshech malei t'lalim,
Pikh el haboker shoshana,
Ektefenu li.

Layla yored le'at
Veru'ach shoshan' noshva,
Hava elchash lakh shir balat,
Zemer shel ahava.
(repeat)

E - rev shel sho - sha - nim,   Net - ze na el ha - bus - tan,

Mor be - sa - mim u - le - vo - na,   Le - ra - glech mif - tan.

TRANSLATION

Evening of roses,
Let's go out to the grove,
Myrrh, Spices, and Frankincense,
Are a threshold at your feet.

Night falls slowly,
A breeze of roses blows,
Let me whisper a song to you,
A song of love.

At dawn a dove coos,
Your hair is filled with dew,
Your lips are as roses unto the morning,
I will pick them for myself.

ABOUT THE SONG

Meaning 'Evening of Roses', *Erev Shel Shoshanim* is a Hebrew love song which is often used in Jewish wedding ceremonies instead of *Here Comes The Bride*.

Judaism is the oldest of the three monotheistic religions. Its core belief is the belief in one God; its practices are based on this and the series of laws set out in the Torah (the first five books of the Old Testament, itself the Jewish bible) and the Mishna (the oral law). Key Jewish practices include the observance of the sabbath on Saturday and dietary laws such as the prohibitions on eating certain meats including pork.

10. Food, Glorious Food

Words & Music by Lionel Bart

LYRICS

Food, glorious food!
Hot sausage and mustard!
While we're in the mood;
Cold jelly and custard!
Pease pudding and saveloys,
"What next?" is the question.
Rich gentlemen have it, boys:
Indigestion!

Food glorious food!
We're anxious to try it.
Three banquets a day:
Our favourite diet!
Just picture a great big steak,
Fried roasted or stewed!
Oh food, wonderful food, marvellous food,
Glorious food!

Food, glorious food!
Don't care what it looks like.
Burned, underdone, crude;
Don't care what the cook's like!
Just thinking of growing fat,
Our senses are reeling.
One moment of knowing that
Full up feeling!

Food glorious food!
We're anxious to try it.
Three banquets a day:
Our favourite diet!
Just picture a great big steak,
Fried roasted or stewed!
Oh food, wonderful food, marvellous food,
Glorious food!

Moderately

Food, glo-ri-ous food! Hot sau-sage and mus-tard! While we're in the mood; cold jel-ly and cus-tard! Pease pud-ding and sa-ve-loys, "What next?" is the ques-tion.

LYRICS

A Froggy went a-courting and he did ride,
    ah-hum, ah-hum, *(x2)*
A froggy went a-courting and he did ride,
Sword and pistol by his side, a-hum, a-hum.

He rode up to Miss Mousie's door,
    ah-hum, ah-hum, *(x2)*
He rode up to Miss Mousie's door
Where he had been many times before,
    ah-hum, ah-hum.

He took Miss Mousie on his knee,
    ah-hum, a-hum, *(x2)*
He took Miss Mousie on his knee, ah-hum, a-hum,
He said, "Miss Mouse, will you marry me?"

"Without my Uncle Rat's consent,"
    a-hum, a-hum, *(x2)*
"Without my Uncle Rat's consent," a-hum, a-hum,
"I wouldn't marry the President," a-hum, a-hum.

Uncle Rat, he laughed and shook his sides,
    a-hum, a-hum, *(x2)*
Uncle Rat, he laughed and shook his sides,
    a-hum, a-hum,
To think his niece would be a bride, a-hum, a-hum.

"Where will the wedding breakfast be?"
    A-hum, a-hum, *(x2)*
"Where will the wedding breakfast be?"
    A-hum, a-hum,
"Way down yonder in the hollow tree."
    A-hum, a-hum.

They all went sailing on the lake,
    a-hum, a-hum, *(x2)*
They all went sailing on the lake, a-hum, a-hum,
And got swallowed up by a big fat snake.
    A-hum, a-hum.

There's bread and cheese upon the shelf,
    a-hum, a-hum, *(x2)*
There's bread and cheese upon the shelf,
    a-hum, a-hum,
If you want anymore you can sing it yourself.
    A-hum, a-hum.

24

11. Froggy Went A-Courting

Traditional

12. God Is So Good

Traditional

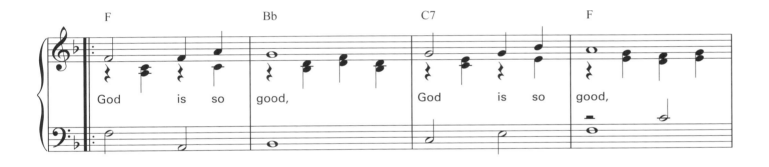

God   is   so   good,   God   is   so   good,

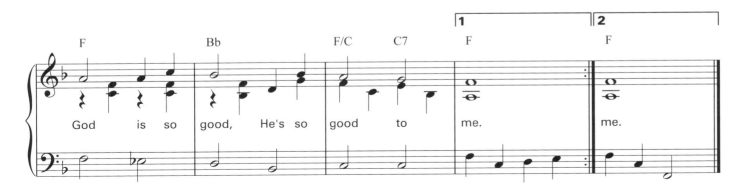

God   is   so   good,   He's so   good   to   me.   me.

LYRICS

God is so good,
God is so good,
God is so good,
He's so good to me.
(repeat)

ABOUT THE SONG

This is a hymn, which is a type of religious song in praise of God or a saint, and usually sung in church. If you've ever been to church on a Sunday morning it's more than likely that you have sung one, or you might have sung hymns at school.

ACTIVITIES

Can you find a way to translate the song into more languages? Does anyone in your class speak any other languages? Sing it in theirs! Here are the same words translated into four languages, to get you started!

French:
Dieu est si bon,
Dieu est si bon,
Dieu est si bon,
Il est si bon pour moi.

German:
Gott ist so gut,
Gott ist so gut,
Gott ist so gut,
Er ist so gut zu mir.

Spanish:
Dios es tan bueno,
Dios es tan bueno,
Dios es tan bueno,
Es tan bueno con migo.

LYRICS

The harp that once through Tara's halls
Its soul of music shed,
Now hangs as mute on Tara's walls
As if that soul were fled.
So sleeps the pride of former days,
So glory's thrill is o'er,
And hearts that once beat high for praise
Now feel that pulse no more.

No more to chiefs and ladies bright
The harp of Tara swells;
The chord alone that breaks the night
Its tale of ruin tells;
Thus Freedom now so seldom wakes;
The only throb she gives
Is when some heart indignant breaks
To show that still she lives.

ABOUT HARPS

The harp is a stringed instrument of which there are many different types. The most recognisable is the large concert harp which is used in classical music. It is plucked like a guitar only there are many more strings, so many that the instrument is very large and must stand on the floor! A person who plays the harp is called a 'harpist'. A smaller harp is used in Ireland. It works in the same way only it has fewer strings.

13. The Harp That Once Through Tara's Halls

Words by Thomas Moore
Traditional Irish Melody

Fairly slow

14. He's Got The Whole World In His Hands

Traditional

Rhythmically

He's got the whole world_ in His hands,_ he's got the whole world in His hands, He's got the whole world in His hands, He's got the whole world in His hands. He's got____ hands.

LYRICS

He's got the whole world in His hands,
He's got the whole world in His hands,
He's got the whole world in His hands,
He's got the whole world in His hands.

He's got you and me, brother, in His hands,
He's got you and me, brother, in His hands,
He's got you and me, brother, in His hands,
He's got the whole world in His hands.

He's got the sun and the moon in His hands,
He's got the sun and the moon in His hands,
He's got the sun and the moon in His hands,
He's got the whole world in His hands.

He's got everyone here in His hands,
He's got everyone here in His hands,
He's got everyone here in His hands,
He's got the whole world in His hands.

LYRICS

Just what makes that little ol' ant
Think he'll move that rubber tree plant
Anyone knows an ant can't
Move a rubber tree plant.

But he's got high hopes,
He's got high hopes,
He's got high apple pie in the sky hopes.
So any time you're getting' low,
'stead of lettin' go,
Just remember that ant.
Oops! There goes another rubber tree plant.

Once there was a silly ol' ram,
Thought he'd punch a hole in a dam;
No one could make that ram scram,
He kept buttin' that dam.

'Cause he had high hopes,
He had high hopes;
He had high apple pie in the sky hopes.
So any time you're feelin' bad,
Stead of feelin' sad,
Just remember that ram.
Oops! There goes a billion kilowatt dam.

So keep your high hopes,
Keep your high hopes;
Keep those high apple pie in the sky hopes.
A problem's just a toy balloon,
They'll be bursting soon,
They're just bound to go "pop!"
Oops! There goes another problem, kerplop!

15. High Hopes

Words by Sammy Cahn
Music by James Van Heusen

Moderately (with a beat)

ABOUT THE SONG

A Hole In The Head was a Broadway play from 1957, and was made into a film in 1959. It featured Frank Sinatra who subsequently popularised the song *High Hopes*. It won an Academy Award for 'Best Original Song' in 1989.

29

I have a dream, a song to sing
To help me cope with anything.
If you see the wonder of a fairytale
You can take the future even if you fail.

I believe in angels,
Something good in ev'rything I see.
I believe in angels
When I know the time is right for me.
I'll cross the stream, I have a dream.

I have a dream, a fantasy
To help me through reality.
And my destination makes it worth the while,
Pushing through the darkness, still another mile.

I believe in angels,
Something good in ev'rything I see.
I believe in angels
When I know the time is right for me.
I'll cross the stream, I have a dream.
I'll cross the stream, I have a dream.

16. I Have A Dream

Words & Music by Benny Andersson & Björn Ulvaeus

Easy Ballad Style

ABOUT THE SONG

The Swedish band ABBA was, and is still, one of the most famous bands in the world. The name was derived from the initial of each of their Christian names (Anni-Frid, Benny, Björn and Agnetha). *I Have A Dream* is one of their many hits, just as popular now as when it was released in 1979.

LYRICS

I used to think that I could not go on,
And life was nothing but an awful song.
But now I know the meaning of true love,
I'm leaning on the everlasting arms.
If I can see it, then I can do it.
If I just believe it, there's nothing to it.

I believe I can fly,
I believe I can touch the sky.
I think about it every night and day,
Spread my wings and fly away.
I believe I can soar,
See me running through that open door.
I believe I can fly,
I believe I can fly,
I believe I can fly.

I was on the verge of breaking down.
Sometimes silence can seem so loud.
There are miracles in life I must achieve,
But first I know it starts inside of me.
If I can see it, then I can be it,
If I just believe it, there's nothing to it.

I believe I can fly,
I believe I can touch the sky.
I think about it every night and day,
Spread my wings and fly away.
I believe I can soar,
See me running through that open door.
I believe I can fly,
I believe I can fly,
I believe I can fly.

17. I Believe I Can Fly

Words & Music by R Kelly

Moderately slow

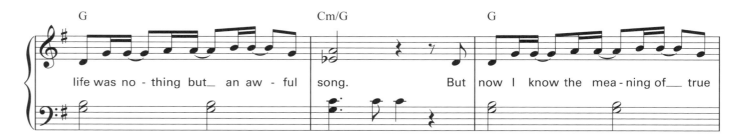

ABOUT THE SONG

This song was written by the R&B artist R. Kelly. It is a hopeful song about overcoming adversity and finding love. Released in 1996, it was number one on the popular music charts in many countries and was used on the film *Space Jam*.

I know an old lady who swallowed a fly,
I don't know why she swallowed a fly –
   Perhaps she'll die!

I know an old lady who swallowed a spider,
That wriggled and jiggled and tickled inside her;
She swallowed the spider to catch the fly;
I don't know why she swallowed a fly –
   Perhaps she'll die!

I know an old lady who swallowed a bird;
How absurd to swallow a bird.
She swallowed the bird to catch the spider,
She swallowed the spider to catch the fly;
I don't know why she swallowed a fly –
   Perhaps she'll die!

I know an old lady who swallowed a cat;
Fancy that to swallow a cat!
She swallowed the cat to catch the bird,
She swallowed the bird to catch the spider,
She swallowed the spider to catch the fly;
I don't know why she swallowed a fly –
   Perhaps she'll die!

I know an old lady that swallowed a dog;
What a hog, to swallow a dog;
She swallowed the dog to catch the cat,
She swallowed the cat to catch the bird,
She swallowed the bird to catch the spider,
She swallowed the spider to catch the fly;
I don't know why she swallowed a fly –
   Perhaps she'll die!

I know an old lady who swallowed a cow,
I don't know how she swallowed a cow;
She swallowed the cow to catch the dog,
She swallowed the dog to catch the cat,
She swallowed the cat to catch the bird,
She swallowed the bird to catch the spider,
She swallowed the spider to catch the fly;
I don't know why she swallowed a fly –
   Perhaps she'll die!

I know an old lady who swallowed a horse...
She's dead, of course!

18. I Know An Old Lady Who Swallowed A Fly

Words by Rose Bonne
Music by Alan Mills

ABOUT THE SONG

This is a nonsense story about an old lady who swallowed lots of animals, each slightly bigger than the last, to catch the previous one. In the end she's eaten so many that are so big, that she dies, of course!

PERFORMANCE

This is a bit of a tongue twister to sing! Make sure that the words are crisp and clear. Singing the consonants clearly and articulated is key to performing this song well. Enjoy singing them with vigour!

LYRICS

It takes a hundred years for a forest tree to grow.
A giant in the sky, climbing way up high
Growing in the earth below.
But by the time I've sung my song
A thousand trees like these will be gone

How long will it be before you can see
That what you are doing is wrong?
How long will it be before you can see
That what you're doing is wrong?

It takes ten thousand years for a forest tribe
   to know
The secrets of the flowers their magical powers,
Growing in the earth below.
But by the time I've sung my song
A thousand flowers like these will be gone.

How long will it be before you can see
That what you are doing is wrong?
How long will it be before you can see
That what you're doing is wrong?

19. It Takes A Hundred Years
(from 'The Emerald Crown')

Words & Music by Debbie Campbell

ABOUT THE SONG

This song is about the destruction of the rainforests by people for wood. The consequences of this leaves animals without homes, the ecosystem in disarray, the disappearance of rare species of plants and animals, hundreds and even thousands of years growth and natural development destroyed.
It is from the musical *The Emerald Crown*, by Debbie Campbell (also published by Novello – NOV079013).

DISCUSS

Where in the world would you find a rainforest?
What animals live in a rainforest?
What are people doing to protect the environment, could the class do more?

37

LYRICS

And did those feet in ancient time
Walk upon England's mountains green?
And was the holy Lamb of God
On England's pleasant pastures seen?
And did the Countenance Divine
Shine forth upon our clouded hills?
And was Jerusalem builded here
Among those dark Satanic mills?

Bring me my bow of burning gold!
Bring me my arrows of desire!
Bring me my spear! O clouds, unfold!
Bring me my chariot of fire!
I will not cease from mental fight,
Nor shall my sword sleep in my hand,
Till we have built Jerusalem
In England's green and pleasant land.

20. Jerusalem

Words by William Blake
Music by Hubert Parry

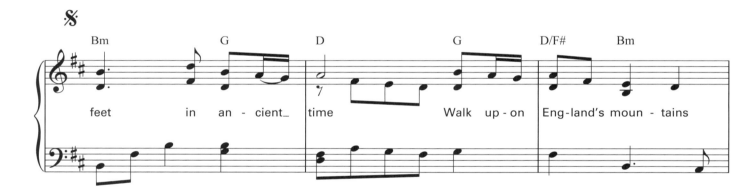

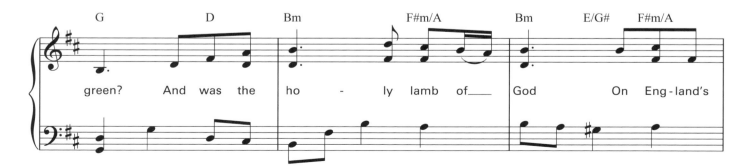

To Coda

D.S. al Coda

Coda

ABOUT THE SONG

This song is a musical setting of a poem by William Blake (1757–1827). It deals with the effects of the industrial revolution, and uses the capital of the Holy Land (Jerusalem) as a metaphor for humanity. In 1916 Hubert Parry set the words to music, creating one of the best-loved hymns in the English language. Its popularity is such that it is played at the Last Night of the Proms at the Royal Albert Hall in London every year and watched on TV by millions worldwide.

ACTIVITIES

Discuss the poem – did Jesus really visit England? What is Blake talking about? The class could write their own poems about England and what they hope it could be like.

LYRICS

The flies are buzzing and the bees are humming
Buzz, buzz, hum, hum.
The doves are cooing and the cows are mooing
Coo, moo, hum, hum.

The flies are buzzing and the bees are humming
Buzz, buzz, hum, hum.
The frogs are croaking and the ducks are quacking
Croak, quack, hum, hum.

PERFORMANCE

Make your buzz, hum, coo, moo, croak, quack
noises sound like the animals and creatures!

Add your own percussion. Can you find
instruments that fit the animal sounds?

21. Hum, Hum!

Words & Music by Carol Barratt

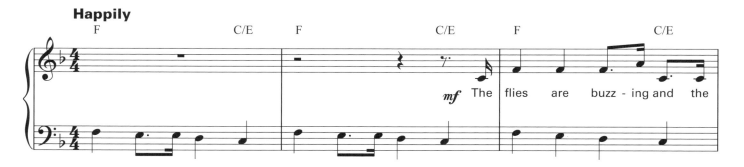

22. Kookaburra Sits In The Old Gum Tree

Words & Music by Marion Sinclair

Bright and bouncy

LYRICS

Kookaburra sits on an old gum tree,
Merry, merry, King of the bush is he,
Laugh, kookaburra,
Laugh, kookaburra,
Gay your life must be.

ABOUT THE SONG

Written in 1934, this was the winning entry in a song-writing competition held by the Girl Guides Association of Victoria, Australia. It is now a popular nursery rhyme, and known across the world.

Caspar, Melchior, Balthazar,
We're three wise men, that's who we are.
We've read the signs up in the heavens:
A King is born who requires our presents.
We three guys are awful wise,
So listen up when we advise:
If you desire a royal connection,
You're heading off in the wrong direction!

Come and meet the king
Who doesn't own a single thing!
He's never been on a magazine;
Rich and famous ain't his scene.
Come and meet a star,
Who'll like you just the way you are!
Don't have to wear no diamond ring,
Jus' listen to what we wise men sing.
Why not come and meet the groovy King
    without a thing?

Caspar, Melchior, Balthazar,
We're three wise men who've travelled far.
We've looked in all the high class places
For newborn kings, but we found no traces.
We three guys then asked around;
At Bethlehem's where he'll be found.
So why not join our delegation
And try your hand at some adoration?

Come and meet the king
Who doesn't own a single thing!
He's never been on a magazine;
Rich and famous ain't his scene.
Come and meet a star,
Who'll like you just the way you are!
Don't have to wear no diamond ring,
Jus' listen to what we wise men sing.
Why not come and meet the groovy King
    without a thing?

23. King Without A Thing
(from 'Manger Tom')

Words by Thomas Allain-Chapman
Music by Richard Allain

ABOUT THE SONG

Jesus was born in a stable, without any of the possessions that kings normally have, like palaces or gold. The song is taken from *Manger Tom*, a nativity musical, telling the Christmas story, through fantastic catchy songs like this. (Also published by Novello – NOV020768).

LYRICS

Oh! Land of my fathers, the land of the free,
The home of the telyn, so soothing to me;
Thy noble defenders were gallant and brave,
For freedom their heart's life they gave.

Wales, Wales, home, sweet home is Wales.
Till death be passed, my love shall last,
My longing, my yearning for Wales.

Thou Eden of bards, and birthplace of song,
The sons of thy mountains are valiant and strong;
The voice of thy streamlets is soft to the ear,
The hills and thy valleys, how dear!

Wales, Wales, home, sweet home is Wales.
Till death be passed, my love shall last,
My longing, my yearning for Wales.

Though slighted and scorned by the proud
   and the strong,
The language of Cambria still charms us in song;
The awen survives; nor have envious tales
Yet silenced the harp of dear Wales.

Wales, Wales, home, sweet home is Wales.
Till death be passed, my love shall last,
My longing, my yearning for Wales.

24. Land Of My Fathers
(Hen Wlad Fy Nhadau)

Words by Evan James
Music by James James

ABOUT THE SONG

Land Of My Fathers is an adopted anthem of Wales. Wales is known as 'the land of song', where singing and taking part in a choir are popular hobbies. A line of the song has appeared on the milled edge of some specially-minted £1 coins.

WELSH LYRICS

Mae hen wlad fy nhadau yn annwyl i mi,
Gwlad beirdd a chantorion, enwogion o fri;
Ei gwrol ryfelwyr, gwladgarwyr tra mâd,
Dros ryddid collasant eu gwaed.

Gwlad, gwlad, pleidiol wyf i'm gwlad.
Tra môr yn fur i'r bur hoff bau,
O bydded i'r hen iaith barhau.

Hen Gymru fynyddig, paradwys y bardd,
Pob dyffryn, pob clogwyn, i'm golwg sydd hardd;
Trwy deimlad gwladgarol, mor swynol yw si
Ei nentydd, afonydd, i mi.

Gwlad, gwlad, pleidiol wyf i'm gwlad.
Tra môr yn fur i'r bur hoff bau,
O bydded i'r hen iaith barhau.

Os treisiodd y gelyn fy ngwlad tan ei droed,
Mae hen iaith y Cymry mor fyw ag erioed,
Ni luddiwyd yr awen gan erchyll law brad,
Na thelyn berseiniol fy ngwlad.

Gwlad, gwlad, pleidiol wyf i'm gwlad.
Tra môr yn fur i'r bur hoff bau,
O bydded i'r hen iaith barhau.

LYRICS

Sometimes in our lives
We all have pain, we all have sorrow.
But if we are wise we know that there's
Always tomorrow.

Lean on me, when you're not strong
And I'll be your friend, I'll help you carry on.
For it won't be long, 'til I'm gonna need
Somebody to lean on.

Please swallow your pride,
If I have things you need to borrow.
For no-one can fill those of your needs
That you don't let show.

Lean on me, when you're not strong
And I'll be your friend, I'll help you carry on.
For it won't be long, 'til I'm gonna need
Somebody to lean on.

If there is a load
You have to bear, that you can't carry,
I'm right up the road, I'll share your load
If you just call me.

Lean on me, when you're not strong
And I'll be your friend, I'll help you carry on.
For it won't be long, 'til I'm gonna need
Somebody to lean on.

ABOUT THE SONG

This song was written and sung by Bill Withers, a popular American singer/songwriter and has since been covered by many other artists. Like *With a Little Help From My Friends* (p82) it is about the importance of friends, not being proud, and having the ability to speak out for yourself.

DISCUSS

What qualities are important in friendship?

25. Lean On Me

Words & Music by Bill Withers

26. London Bridge

Traditional

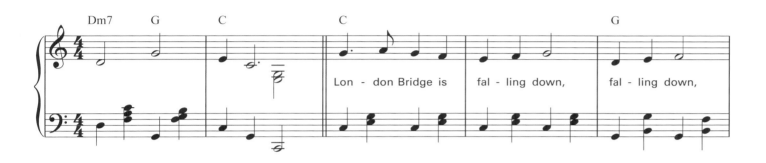

Lon - don Bridge is | fal - ling down, | fal - ling down,

fal - ling down. | Lon - don Bridge is | fal - ling down, | my fair | la - dy.

LYRICS

London Bridge is falling down,
Falling down, falling down.
London Bridge is falling down,
My fair lady.

Take the key and lock her up,
Lock her up, lock her up.
Take the key and lock her up,
My fair lady.

Build it up with silver and gold,
Silver and gold, silver and gold.
Build it up with silver and gold,
My fair lady.

Gold and silver I have none,
I have none, I have none.
Gold and silver I have none,
My fair lady.

ABOUT THE SONG

London Bridge today is not the same structure the song would have been written about. There have been many bridges on the same spot, the first almost 2,000 years ago, built by the Romans. An American businessman bought the bridge to go across Lake Havasu in Arizona and took it there in pieces.

PERCUSSION

Add some percussion instruments to this song, like a Cabasa and a Tambourine. Here is a rhythm that could be used:

My grandfather's clock was too large for the shelf,
So it stood ninety years on the floor.
It was taller by half than the old man himself,
Though it weighed not a pennyweight more.
It was bought on the morn of the day that he was born,
And was always his treasure and pride.
But it stopped short, never to go again,
When the old man died.

Ninety years without slumbering, tick-tock, tick-tock,
His life seconds numbering, tick-tock, tick-tock,
But it stopped short, never to go again,
When the old man died.

In watching its pendulum swing to and fro,
Many years had he spent while a boy;
And in childhood and manhood the clock
    seemed to know,
And to share both his grief and his joy.
For it struck twenty-four when he entered at the door
With a blooming and beautiful bride.
But it stopped short, never to go again,
When the old man died.

Ninety years without slumbering, tick-tock, tick-tock...

My grandfather said that of those he could hire,
Not a servant so faithful he found;
For it wasted no time, and had but one desire -
At the close of each week to be wound.
And it kept in its place, not a frown upon its face,
And the hands never hung by its side.
But it stopped short, never to go again,
When the old man died.

Ninety years without slumbering, tick-tock, tick-tock...

It rang an alarm in the dead of the night,
An alarm that for years had been dumb;
And we knew that his spirit was pluming for flight,
That his hour of departure had come.
Still the clock kept the time, with a soft and
    muffled chime,
As we silently stood by his side.
But it stopped short, never to go again,
When the old man died.

Ninety years without slumbering, tick-tock, tick-tock...

48

27. My Grandfather's Clock

Words & Music by Henry Clay Work

Moderately

LYRICS

To Bombay a travelling circus came.
They brought an intelligent elephant
And Nellie was her name.
One dark night she slipped her iron chain
And off she ran to Hindustan
And was never seen again.

Nellie the Elephant packed her trunk
And said goodbye to the circus,
Off she went with a trumpety trump,
Trump, trump, trump.
Nellie the Elephant packed her trunk
And trundled back to the jungle.
Off she went with a trumpety trump
Trump, trump, trump

The head of the herd was calling
Far, far away.
They met one night in the silver light
On the road to Mandalay.
So Nellie the Elephant packed her trunk
And said goodbye to the circus,
Off she went with a trumpety trump,
Trump, trump, trump.

Night by night she danced to the circus band
When Nellie was leading the big parade
She looked so proud and grand.
No more tricks for Nellie to perform,
They taught her how to take a bow
And she took the crowd by storm.

Nellie the Elephant packed her trunk
And said goodbye to the circus...

28. Nellie The Elephant

Words by Ralph Butler
Music by Peter Hart

PAUSE FOR THOUGHT

Why did Nellie run away from the circus?
Is it right to tame wild animals for shows,
to entertain people?

29. Please Mr Organ-Man

Words by Marian Lines
Music by Betty Roe

Comfortable waltz

1. Please, Mis-ter Or-gan-Man, play us a tune, As light and as bright as a yel-low bal-loon. Ting-a-ling-ting, ting-a-ling-tong, Grind us a ting-a-ling song; Please, Mis-ter Or-gan-Man, play us a tune.

LYRICS

Please, Mister Organ-Man, play us a tune,
As light and as bright as a yellow balloon.
Ting-a-ling-ting, ting-a-ling-tong,
Grind us a ting-a-ling song;
Please, Mister Organ-Man, play us a tune.

Please, Mister Organ-Man, sing us a song,
Then teach us the words as we're humming along.
Jing-a-ling-june, jing-a-ling-june,
Grind us a jing-a-ling tune;
Please, Mister Organ-Man, sing us a song.

Please, Mister-Organ Man, lead us a dance,
And show us the steps as we leap and we prance.
Tip-a-tip-tap, tip-a-tip-tap,
Grind us a slip-a-tip-tap;
Please, Mister Organ-Man, lead us a dance.

ABOUT THE SONG

An 'Organ Man' or 'Organ Grinder' was someone found on the streets of 19th-century Europe. Street organs were operated by turning a handle on the side as perforated paper which created the notes was fed through it. They would play popular tunes of the day, including opera.

The song is from a school musical called *The Barnstormers*, set on a Victorian farm, it is about a play put on by the local villagers (also published by Novello – NOV390071).

30. On Ilkley Moor Baht 'At

Traditional

LYRICS

Where 'as tha bin since I saw thee?
On Ilkley Moor baht 'at.
Where 'as tha bin since I saw thee?
Where 'as tha bin since I saw thee?

On Ilkley Moor baht 'at.
On Ilkley Moor baht 'at.
On Ilkley Moor baht 'at.

Tha'll go and get thee death o' cold.
On Ilkley Moor baht 'at.
Tha'll go and get thee death o' cold.
Tha'll go and get thee death o' cold.

On Ilkley Moor baht 'at.
On Ilkley Moor baht 'at.
On Ilkley Moor baht 'at.

Then we shall have to bury thee.
On Ilkley Moor baht 'at.
Then we shall have to bury thee.
Then we shall have to bury thee.

On Ilkley Moor baht 'at.
On Ilkley Moor baht 'at.
On Ilkley Moor baht 'at.

Then t'worms'll come and eat thee up.
On Ilkley Moor baht 'at.
Then t'worms'll come and eat thee up.
Then t'worms'll come and eat thee up.

On Ilkley Moor baht 'at.
On Ilkley Moor baht 'at.
On Ilkley Moor baht 'at.

That's where we gets our own back.
On Ilkley Moor baht 'at.
That's where we gets our own back.
That's where we gets our own back.

On Ilkley Moor baht 'at.
On Ilkley Moor baht 'at.
On Ilkley Moor baht 'at.

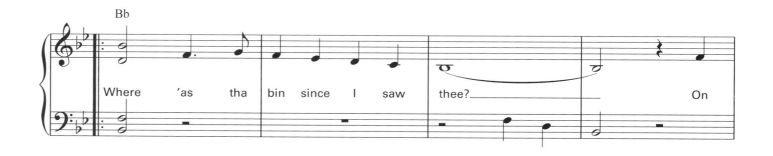

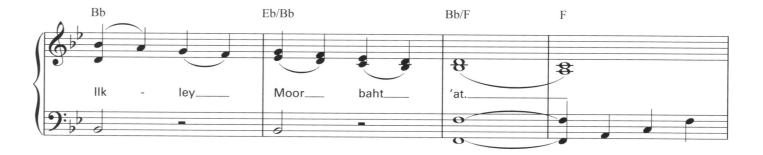

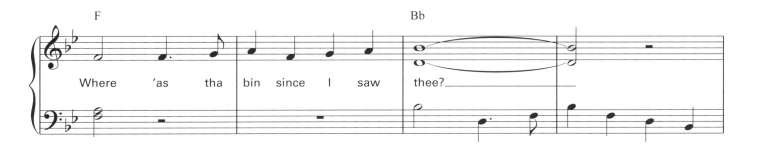

Where 'as tha bin since I saw thee?

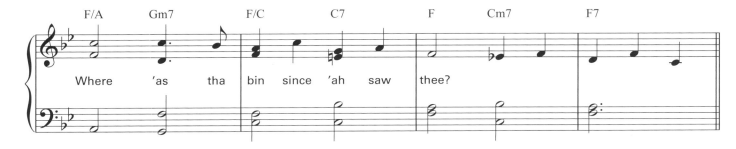

Where 'as tha bin since 'ah saw thee?

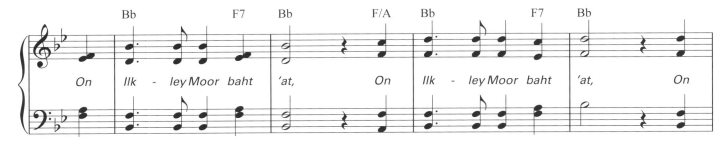

On Ilk - ley Moor baht 'at, On Ilk - ley Moor baht 'at, On

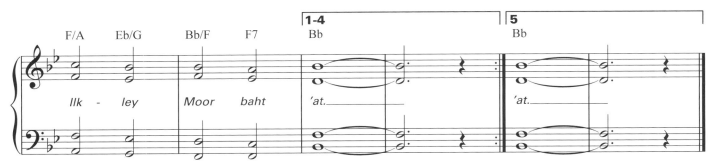

1-4

Ilk - ley Moor baht 'at.

5

'at.

ABOUT THE SONG

Ilkley is a town in Yorkshire, situated on the edge of the Yorkshire Dales. Ilkley Moor is a vast area of land to the south of the town. It is high up and not many people live there. The song should be called 'On Ilkley Moor Without A Hat' but in this case it is written how people in Yorkshire would pronounce it!

MODERN LYRICS

This is a full translation of the song into modern English:

Where have you been since I last saw you?
On Ilkley Moor without a hat.
Where have you been since I last saw you?
Where have you been since I last saw you?

On Ilkley Moor without a hat.
On Ilkley Moor without a hat.
On Ilkley Moor without a hat.

You are bound to catch your death of cold...

Then we will have to bury you...

Then the worms will come and eat you up...

That's where we get our own back...

LYRICS

"Oranges and lemons"
Say the bells of St. Clement's.

"You owe me five farthings"
Say the bells of St. Martin's.

"When will you pay me?"
Say the bells of Old Bailey.

"When I grow rich!"
Say the bells of Shoreditch.

"When will that be?"
Say the bells of Stepney.

"I do not know!"
Says the great bell of Bow.

Here comes a candle to light you to bed.
And here comes a chopper to chop off your head!

31. Oranges And Lemons

Words & Music by Cecil James Sharp

ABOUT THE SONG

This is one of the most popular nursery rhymes in the United Kingdom. The meanings of the words are not simply referring to bells of London churches but are about criminals who are put in jail. It is said to be written specifically about the prisoners of Newgate Prison, a place largely full of debtors ('"When will you pay me?" say the Bells of Old Bailey'). The coming of the candle 'to light you to bed' was when a candle was lit outside the cell of a prisoner, signifying that they would be the next to have their heads chopped off.

ACTIONS

Two children make an arch by putting their arms in the air, to a point, fingertips touching. Everyone else walks through the arch, while the song is being sung. When it comes to the final line of the song the two making the arch bring their arms down over the person who is currently walking through, trapping them. When each verse is completed, the person who got trapped takes over from the arch couple with somebody else of their choosing.

LYRICS

When the world leaves you feeling blue,
You can count on me, I will be there for you.
When it seems all your hopes and dreams
Are a million miles away, I will reassure you.
We gotta all stick together.
Good friends, there for each other.
Never ever forget that I got you and you got me.

So reach for the stars.
Climb ev'ry mountain higher
Reach for the stars.
Follow your heart's desire.
Reach for the stars.
And when that rainbow's shining over you,
That's when your dreams will all come true.

There's a place waiting just for you.
It's a special place where your dreams
   all come true.
Fly away, swim the ocean blue.
Drive that open road, leave the past behind you.
Don't stop, gotta keep movin'.
Your hopes gotta keep building.
Never ever forget that I got you and you got me.

So reach for the stars.
Climb ev'ry mountain higher
Reach for the stars.
Follow your heart's desire.
Reach for the stars.
And when that rainbow's shining over you,
That's when your dreams will all come true.

32. Reach

Words & Music by Cathy Dennis & Andrew Todd

ABOUT THE SONG

This was one of the pop group S Club 7's most successful songs, reaching No. 2 in the UK charts. It is about friendship, aiming high, striving to achieve, and following dreams.

ACTIONS

Each time the word 'Reach' is sung, hands and arms should be thrown straight up into the air (as if reaching to the sky). On the following beat everyone clap their hands.

LYRICS

Raindrops keep fallin' on my head,
And just like the guy whose feet are too big for
  his bed,
Nothin' seems to fit.
Those raindrops are fallin' on my head.
They keep fallin'!

So I just did me some talkin' to the sun,
And I said I didn't like the way he got things done.
Sleepin' on the job.
Those raindrops are fallin' on my head.
They keep fallin'!

But there's one thing I know,
The blues he sends to meet me won't defeat me.
It won't be long till happiness steps up to greet me.

Raindrops keep fallin' on my head,
But that doesn't mean my eyes will soon be
  turnin' red.
Cryin's not for me
'Cause I'm never gonna stop the rain
  by complainin'.
Because I'm free,
Nothing's botherin' me.

33. Raindrops Keep Fallin' On My Head

Words by Hal David
Music by Burt Bacharach

Rhythmically

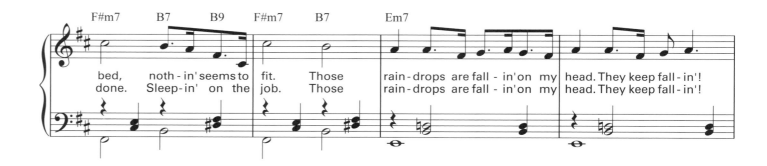

ABOUT THE SONG

Burt Bacharach wrote this song for the cowboy film *Butch Cassidy And The Sundance Kid*. It is popular all over the world and has achieved success being sung by many different singers. Bacharach is a famous songwriter with many popular hits to his name.

DISCUSS

Does the music from this song remind you of rain? If so, then why?

CD

There is a two bar introduction on the CD, using bars 18 and 19.

61

34. Right Said Fred

Words by Myles Rudge
Music by Ted Dicks

D.S. al Coda
(see lyric block)

✛ **Coda**

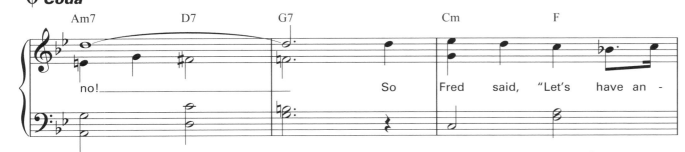

D.C. *(all repeats for Verse 2)*

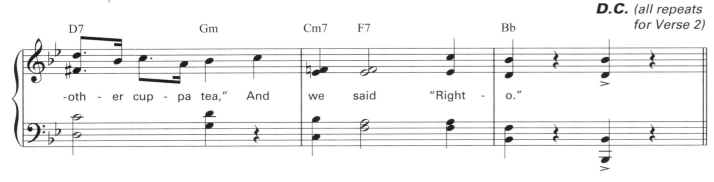

ABOUT THE SONG

This song is about three useless removal men who are attempting to move a piano through a doorway that is too small! They try all sorts of things from making the piano smaller to dismantling other things, like the door!

LYRICS

Shout, shout, shout for happiness,
There's no joy unless you
Shout for happiness all day through, oh!

Sing, sing, let your voices ring,
Bid your troubles adieu.
Take the joy that is meant for you.

Don't sit in the corner like Jackie Horner,
Get where the bright lights are.
Just look up high, search the sky,
Find your guiding star.

Shout, shout, shout for happiness,
There's no joy if you're blue.
Shout for happiness all day through.

35. Shout For Happiness

Words & Music by Jack Hart & Tom Blight

HISTORY

This song was originally sung by Al Bowlly who was a popular jazz singer of the 1930s. Bowlly was credited with inventing 'The Modern Singing Style' or what is more commonly known as 'crooning', popularised by the likes of Bing Crosby and Frank Sinatra. He is also seen as the first pop star.

ACTIONS

Get the class to decide on different actions for the words 'sing' and 'shout', to be performed each time the words are repeated.

36. Show Me The Way To Go Home

Words & Music by Irving King & Hal Swain

LYRICS

When I'm happy, when I'm happy,
Singing all the while.
I don't need nobody then,
To show me how to smile.
When I've been out on a spree,
Toddling down the street.
With this little melody ev'ryone I greet.

Show me the way to go home,
I'm tired and I want to go to bed.
Had a little drink a-bout an hour a-go,
And it's gone right to my head.
Where ever I may roam,
On land, or sea, or foam.
You can always hear me singing this song,
Show me the way to go home.

Old King Cole was a merry old soul,
And a merry old soul was he.
He called for his wine, and he called for his pipe,
And he called for his fiddlers three.
When they'd had a high old time,
All the whole night through,
What was it that King Cole said,
And his fiddlers too?

Show me the way to go home,
I'm tired and I want to go to bed.
Had a little drink a-bout an hour a-go,
And it's gone right to my head.
Where ever I may roam,
On land, or sea, or foam.
You can always hear me singing this song,
Show me the way to go home.

LYRICS

The sun has got his hat on,
Hip hip hip hooray!
The sun has got his hat on,
And he's coming out today.

Now we'll all be happy,
Hip hip hip hooray!
The sun has got his hat on,
And he's coming out today.

He's been tanning tourists
Out in Timbuktu.
Now he's coming back
To do the same to you.

Jump into your sunbath,
Hip hip hip hooray!
The sun has got his hat on,
And is coming out today.

37. The Sun Has Got His Hat On

Words & Music by Ralph Butler & Noel Gay

Bright beat

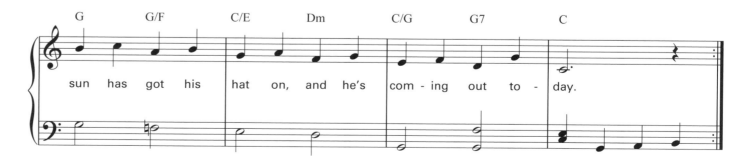

ABOUT THE SONG

From the 1936 musical *Me And My Girl*, this is a popular and memorable song for people of all ages. A family of aristocrats is looking for an heir to the title of Earl of Hareford. They find the long lost heir, Bill, a Cockney from Lambeth. The musical follows his story of becoming a gentleman. Bill's Cockney girlfriend Sally is disapproved of until they realise how much he loves her.

38. The Salley Gardens

Down by the salley gardens
  my love and I did meet;
She passed the salley gardens
  with little snow-white feet.
She bid me take love easy,
  as the leaves grow on the tree;
But I, being young and foolish,
  with her did not agree.

In a field by the river
  my love and I did stand,
And on my leaning shoulder
  she laid her snow-white hand.
She bid me take life easy,
  as the grass grows on the weirs;
But I was young and foolish,
  and now am full of tears.

Down by the salley gardens
  my love and I did meet;
She passed the salley gardens
  with little snow-white feet.
She bid me take love easy,
  as the leaves grow on the tree;
But I, being young and foolish,
  with her did not agree.

Words by William Butler Yeats
Traditional Music

39. Scarborough Fair

Traditional

LYRICS

Are you going to Scarborough fair?
Parsley, sage, rosemary and thyme.
Remember me to one who lives there.
For once she was a true love of mine.

Tell her to make me a cambric shirt.
Parsley, sage, rosemary and thyme.
Without any seam or fine needlework,
And then she'll be a true love of mine.

Tell her to wash it in yonder dry well,
Parsley, sage, rosemary and thyme;
Where water never have sprung, nor drop
   of rain fell,
And then she'll be a true love of mine.

Oh, will you find me an acre of land,
Parsley, sage, rosemary and thyme;
Between the sea foam and the sea sand
Or never be a true love of mine.

Oh, will you plough it with a lamb's horn,
Parsley, sage, rosemary and thyme;
And sow it all over with one peppercorn,
Or never be a true love of mine.

And when you have done and finished your work,
Parsley, sage, rosemary and thyme;
Then come to me for your cambric shirt,
And you shall be a true love of mine.

ABOUT THE SONG

This is a song about a young man who sets his former lover a series of difficult tasks to complete: make a shirt without a seam then have it washed in a dry well, that he might take her back on completion. She accepts but offers some equally impossible tasks to perform, promising him his seamless shirt when he is finished.

LYRICS

Speed, bonnie boat, like a bird on the wing,
Onward! the sailors cry;
Carry the lad that's born to be King
Over the sea to Skye.

Loud the winds howl, loud the waves roar,
Thunderclaps rend the air;
Baffled, our foes stand by the shore,
Follow they will not dare.

Speed, bonnie boat...

Though the waves leap, soft shall ye sleep,
Ocean's a royal bed.
Rocked in the deep, Flora will keep
Watch by your weary head.

Speed, bonnie boat...

Many's the lad fought on that day,
Well the Claymore could wield,
When the night came, silently lay
Dead in Culloden's field.

Speed, bonnie boat...

Burned are their homes, exile and death
Scatter the loyal men;
Yet ere the sword cool in the sheath
Charlie will come again.

Speed, bonnie boat...

ABOUT THE SONG

This song tells the story of Bonnie Prince Charlie of Scotland, and his escape after defeat at the battle of Culloden in 1746. It is said that he rowed to the Isle of Skye disguised as a serving maid! A traditional Scottish song, it was only conceived in the form we know at the very end of the 19th century, although it is based on a much older folk melody.

40. The Skye Boat Song

Traditional

41. Sur Le Pont d'Avignon

Traditional

Moderately

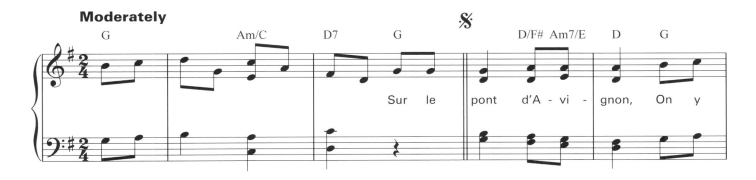

Sur le pont d'A - vi - gnon, On y

dan - se, on y dan - se, Sur le pont d'A - vi - gnon, On y dan - se tout en rond.

Fine

Slower, with actions

D.S. as required, then Fine

1. Les jeunes filles font comme çi, Les garç-ons font comme ça. Sur le

LYRICS

Sur le pont d'Avignon,
On y danse, on y danse,
Sur le pont d'Avignon,
On y danse tout en rond.

Les jeunes filles font comme çi,
Les garçons font comme ça.

Sur le pont d'Avignon...

Les poupees font comme çe,
Les soldats font comme ça.

Sur le pont d'Avignon...

Les grenouilles font comme çi,
Les gorilles font comme ça.

Sur le pont d'Avignon...

TRANSLATION

On the bridge of Avignon,
Everyone is dancing, everyone is dancing,
On the bridge of Avignon,
Everyone is dancing, everyone is dancing.

The young girls go like that,
The boys go like that.

On the bridge...

The dolls go like this,
The soldiers go like that.

On the bridge...

The frogs go like this,
The gorillas go like that.

On the bridge...

LYRICS

Down in the meadow in a little bitty pool
Lived three little fishes and a momma fishy too.
"Swim" said the momma fishy, swim if you can,
And they swam and they swam all over the dam.

Boop boop, dittem, dottem waddem, shh.
Boop boop, dittem, dottem waddem, shh.
Boop boop, dittem, dottem waddem, shh.
And they swam and they swam all over the dam.

"Stop," said the momma fishy, or you will get lost,
But the three little fishes didn't want to be bossed.
The three little fishes went off on a spree,
And they swam and they swam right out to the sea.

Boop boop, dittem, dottem waddem, shh.
Boop boop, dittem, dottem waddem, shh.
Boop boop, dittem, dottem waddem, shh.
And they swam and they swam all over the dam.

"Wee!" yelled the little fishes, here's a lot of fun.
We'll swim in the sea till the day is done.
They swam and they swam, it was a lark,
Till all of a sudden they met a shark!

Boop boop, dittem, dottem waddem, shh.
Boop boop, dittem, dottem waddem, shh.
Boop boop, dittem, dottem waddem, shh.
And they swam and they swam all over the dam.

"Help!" cried the little fishes, look at all the whales,
And quick as they could they turned on their tails.
Back to the pool in the meadow they swam,
And they swam and they swam back over the dam.

Boop boop, dittem, dottem waddem, shh.
Boop boop, dittem, dottem waddem, shh.
Boop boop, dittem, dottem waddem, shh.
And they swam and they swam all over the dam.

42. Three Little Fishes

Words & Music by Saxie Dowell

ABOUT THE SONG

This is a story of three young fishes who try to 'run before they can walk'! The mother fish tells them to swim in the pond but the young fishes get carried away and swim out to sea, where they almost get eaten by a shark. Then they swim straight back to the pond.

PERFORMANCE

The words in this chorus are great to sing – enjoy the sounds the consonants make. Create some actions for each of the following:

Boop boop
Dittem dottem
Waddem
Shh

43. Top Of The World

LYRICS

Such a feelin's comin' over me,
There is wonder in 'most ev'rything I see,
Not a cloud in the sky, got the sun in my eyes,
And I won't be surprised if it's a dream.
Ev'rything I want the world to be,
Is now coming true especially for me,
And the reason is clear, it's because you are here,
You're the nearest thing to heaven that I've seen.

I'm on the top of the world lookin'
    down on creation,
And the only explanation I can find,
Is the love that I've found,
    ever since you've been around,
Your love's put me at the top of the world.

Something in the wind has learned my name,
And it's tellin' me that things are not the same,
In the leaves on the trees and the touch of
    the breeze,
There's a pleasin' sense of happiness for me.
There is only one wish on my mind,
When this day is through I hope that I will find
That tomorrow will be just the same for you
    and me,
All I need will be mine if you are here.

I'm on the top of the world lookin'
    down on creation,
And the only explanation I can find,
Is the love that I've found,
    ever since you've been around,
Your love's put me at the top of the world.

Words by John Bettis
Music by Richard Carpenter

44. When You Believe
(from 'The Prince Of Egypt')

Words & Music by Stephen Schwartz

ABOUT THE SONG

From the film *The Prince Of Egypt*, this song was originally sung by Mariah Carey and Whitney Houston. The film is about Moses, the Prince of Egypt, in particular where Moses leads the slaves out of Egypt, as told in the book of Exodus.

LYRICS

Who's been polishing the sun,
Brightening the sky today?
They must have known just how I like it,
'Cause ev'rything's going my way.

Who's been teaching all the birds
How to sing a roundelay?
They must have known just how I like it,
'Cause ev'rything's going my way.

Yesterday ev'rything looked anyhow.
Then I met someone and, oh!
Look at it now.

Who's been polishing the sun,
Rubbing out the clouds of grey?
They must have known just how I like it,
'Cause ev'rything's going my way.

45. Who's Been Polishing The Sun

Words & Music by Noel Gay

LYRICS

What would you think if I sang out of tune,
Would you stand up and walk out on me?
Lend me your ears and I'll sing you a song,
And I'll try not to sing out of key.
Oh, I get by with a little help from my friends.
Mm, I get high with a little help from my friends.
Mm, gonna try with a little help from my friends.

What do I do when my love is away,
Does it worry you to be alone?
How do I feel by the end of the day,
Are you sad because you're on your own?
Oh, I get by with a little help from my friends.
Mm, I get high with a little help from my friends.
Mm, gonna try with a little help from my friends.

Do you need anybody?
I need somebody to love.
Could it be anybody?
I want somebody to love.

Would you believe in a love at first sight?
Yes I'm certain that it happens all the time.
What do you see when you turn out the light?
I can't tell you, but I know it's mine.
Oh, I get by with a little help from my friends.
Mm, I get high with a little help from my friends.
Mm, gonna try with a little help from my friends.

Do you need anybody?
I need somebody to love.
Could it be anybody?
I want somebody to love.

46. With A Little Help From My Friends

Words & Music by John Lennon & Paul McCartney

1

2, 3

D   G   D

Mm,_ gon-na try_ with a lit-tle help_ from my friends._

D   Bm   E7   D   C

Do you need_ a-ny-bo - dy? I need some-bo-dy to love._

To Coda ⊕

G   D   Bm   E7   D   C

Could it be_ a-ny-bo - dy? I want some-bo-dy to love._

D.S. al Coda
(Verse 3)

⊕ **Coda**   *rit.*

G   D   Bb   C   D

ABOUT THE SONG

This song was written by John Lennon and Paul McCartney of The Beatles, the band formed in Liverpool in 1960. They are perhaps the most famous and successful pop group of all time. This was an unusual song because it was sung by Ringo Starr, who was the drummer! It expresses the importance of friendship and helping one another.

PAUSE FOR THOUGHT

Who are our friends?
Are we there for our friends when they need us?

47. Ye Banks And Braes

Traditional

LYRICS

Ye banks and braes o' bonnie Doon,
How can ye bloom sae fresh and fair,
How can ye chant ye little birds,
and I sae weary, full o' care.
Ye'll break my heart ye warbling birds,
That wanton through the flow'ry thorn,
Ye mind me o' departed joys,
Departed never to return.

Oft hae I roved by bonnie Doon,
To see the rose and woodbine twine,
And ilk a bird sang o' it's love,
And fondly sae did I o' mine.
Wi' lightsome heart I pulled a rose,
Full sweet upon its thorny tree,
And my false lover stole my rose,
But ah! He left the thorn in me.

ABOUT THE SONG

This is a traditional Scottish song with words by the famous Scottish poet Robert Burns. It is about the pain of lost love, which Burns compares to the thorn of a rose. Banks and Braes are parts of the riverside and surrounding hillside. The song describes the River Doon in Scotland, where Burns grew up.

DISCUSSION

Comparing loves pain to a thorn is a metaphor, which is a figure of speech in which two dissimilar objects that have something important in common are compared: a thorn can be painful, as can love. Can you think of other metaphors?

LYRICS

The other night, dear,
As I lay sleeping,
I dreamed I held you in my arms.
When I awoke, dear,
I was mistaken,
And I hung my head and cried.

You are my sunshine,
My only sunshine,
You make me happy,
When skies are grey.
You'll never know dear
How much I love you.
Please don't take my sunshine away.

I'll always love you
And make you happy
If you will only say the same.
But if you leave me
To love another
You'll regret it all some day.

You are my sunshine,
My only sunshine...

You told me once, dear,
You really loved me
And no-one else could come between.
But now you've left me
And love another.
You have shattered all my dreams.

You are my sunshine,
My only sunshine...

Louisiana, my Louisiana,
The place where I was born.
White fields of cotton -
Green fields of clover,
The best fishing
And long, tall corn.

You are my sunshine,
My only sunshine...

48. You Are My Sunshine

Words & Music by Jimmie Davis & Charles Mitchell

ABOUT THE SONG

In America, *You Are My Sunshine* is considered the state song of Louisiana, because its writing is attributed to a former governor, Jimmie Davis, who was also a country music singer. The final verse is like an advert for Louisiana tourists, saying how wonderful it is!

49. This Beautiful Day

Words & Music by Nanette Workman

LYRICS

Ev'rybody gather round
I got something important to say.
We got a whole lot to be grateful for
On this right beautiful day, O Lord,
On this right beautiful day.

Clap your hands, brother, sing with me,
Take another look around you now.
We've sure not got a lot of love in this world,
Take advantage of the things that we got,
dear brothers,
Take advantage of the things that we got.

Come on brothers and sisters,
Let me see you smile, spreading from ear to ear.
You know as well as me there's been a
Whole lot of crying and complaining 'bout the
way we live.
Don't you think it's about time for a change?
Don't you think we ought to try a little more of
this loving,
Living, laughing giving, singing out and praising
the Lord.
Giving thanks for all the great, beautiful things
That shine around us on this beautiful day, O Lord,
That shine around us on this beautiful day.

(repeat chorus)

PAUSE FOR THOUGHT

This song is about what we have to be grateful for. Life is full of ups and downs, but no matter what, we should always be grateful for our family and friends, our health and all the other wonderful things that make life great!

50. Edward Lear's Round

Words by Edward Lear and Stephen Barlow
Music by Stephen Barlow

LYRICS

Limerick 1 *(Voice 1, sung 4 times)*

There was an old man with a beard,
Who said "It is just as I feared!
Two owls and a hen,
Four larks and a wren,
Have all built their nests in my beard!"

Limerick 2 *(Voice 2, sung 3 times)*

There was an old man of the coast,
Who placidly sat on a post;
But when it was cold
He relinquished his hold
And called for some hot buttered toast.

Limerick 3 *(Voice 3, sung 2 times)*

There was an old person of Ware
Who rode on the back of a bear;
When they ask'd "Does it trot?"
He said "Certainly not!
He's a Moppsikon Floppsikon Bear!"

Accompaniment Voices

Sing Sam sing!
Sing sang song!
Sing Sam sing song
Sing sang song!
(repeat)

Ding dang dong!
Bing bang bong!
Sing Sam sing song
Sing sang song!

Bim bam bom!
Jim jam jom!
Sing Sam sing song
Sing sang song!

PERFORMANCE

This piece is a lot of fun, and very simple. It can be performed in a few different ways, depending on resources. Follow the notes below, to help choose which is best for your group.

1. The limericks can be learned separately by everyone. Or one group can learn just one, and that's the way the 'Round' is written out here. The tune remains the same.

2. All three Limericks can be sung by everyone but in unison (follow the melody of Voice 1, but singing the different limericks as different verses).

3. It can be done in two parts, or even three as written out here. And other limericks can be adapted very slightly to fit the tune.

4. Everyone can also have fun with and learn the accompaniment, a very simple repeating four-bar phrase. No piano is intended, but the accompaniment can be played on a piano, or improvised from the repeating chords F – C. Chime bars/glockenpiels or any other suitable classroom instrument could play this.

5. The vocal accompaniment can be improvised too within the 4 bar shape, try other sounds as well as 'Ding', 'Bong', 'Bam' etc, and other children's names instead of 'Sam'.

More limericks can be learned and sung to this melody.

WHO WAS EDWARD LEAR?

Edward Lear was born in London and was the 20th child of his parents and worked as an artist, illustrator, author and poet. When he was four he had to move out of his family home with his sister (who was 21 years older) because of their failing family fortune. He was very talented and mostly taught himself. He gave some drawing lessons to Queen Victoria for a short time.

Edward Lear wrote a LOT of limericks. People call his type of writing 'literary nonsense' as it uses phrases which don't make sense. Most jokes are funny because they do make sense. But nonsense is often funny because it doesn't!

More limericks can be learned and sung to this melody.

Published by
Novello Publishing Limited
14-15 Berners Street, London, W1T 3LJ, UK.

Exclusive distributors:
Music Sales Limited
Distribution Centre, Newmarket Road,
Bury St Edmunds, Suffolk, IP33 3YB, UK.

Music Sales Pty Limited
20 Resolution Drive, Caringbah,
NSW 2229, Australia.

Order No. NOV492404
ISBN: 978-1-84938-197-0
This book © Copyright 2009
Novello & Company Limited.

Project Editor: Rachel Lindley
Assistant Editor: Oliver Miller
Piano accompaniments played by Jon Ranger.
CD recorded, mixed and mastered by Jonas Persson.
Music Processed by Paul Ewers Music Design.
Inside layout and cover design by Tim Field.
Back cover image: Tara Moore/Getty Images.
Music processed by Paul Ewers Music Design.

Printed in the EU.

Your Guarantee of Quality:
As publishers, we strive to produce every book
to the highest commercial standards.

The book has been carefully designed to
minimise awkward page turns and to make
playing from it a real pleasure.

Particular care has been given to specifying
acid-free, neutral-sized paper made from pulps
which have not been elemental chlorine bleached.

This pulp is from farmed sustainable forests
and was produced with special regard for
the environment.

Throughout, the printing and binding have
been planned to ensure a sturdy, attractive
publication which should give years of enjoyment.

If your copy fails to meet our high standards,
please inform us and we will gladly replace it.

www.musicsales.com

TRACK LISTING

CD1
OM43241

1. **A-ROVING**
   (Traditional)
   Novello & Company Limited

2. **THE ASH GROVE**
   (Traditional)
   Novello & Company Limited

3. **THE ANIMALS WENT IN TWO BY TWO**
   (Traditional)
   Novello & Company Limited

4. **THE BARE NECESSITIES**
   (Gilkyson)
   Warner/Chappell Artemis Music

5. **THE BEST DAY EVER**
   (from 'The SpongeBob SquarePants Movie')
   (Kenny/Paley)
   Sony/ATV Music Publishing (UK) Limited.

6. **DO-RE-MI**
   (Hammerstein/Rodgers)
   EMI Music Publishing Limited.

7. **THE BRITISH GRENADIERS**
   (Traditional)
   Novello & Company Limited

8. **DON'T DILLY DALLY (MY OLD MAN)**
   (Leigh/Collins)
   Novello & Company Limited.

9. **EREV SHEL SHOSHANIM**
   (Dor/Hadar)
   Acum Limited.

10. **FOOD, GLORIOUS FOOD**
    (Bart)
    Lakeview Music Publishing
    Company Limited.

11. **FROGGY WENT A-COURTING**
    (Traditional)
    Novello & Company Limited

12. **GOD IS SO GOOD**
    (Traditional)
    Novello & Company Limited

13. **THE HARP THAT ONCE THROUGH TARA'S HALLS**
    (Traditional/Moore)
    Novello & Company Limited

14. **HE'S GOT THE WHOLE WORLD IN HIS HANDS**
    (Traditional)
    Novello & Company Limited

15. **HIGH HOPES**
    (Cahn/Van Heusen)
    Chelsea Music Publishing
    Company Limited.

16. **I HAVE A DREAM**
    (Andersson/Ulvaeus)
    Bocu Music Limited.

17. **I BELIEVE I CAN FLY**
    (Kelly)
    Imagem Music.

18. **I KNOW AN OLD LADY WHO SWALLOWED A FLY**
    (Bonne/Mills)
    Peermusic (UK) Limited.

19. **IT TAKES A HUNDRED YEARS**
    (Campbell)
    Novello & Company Limited

20. **JERUSALEM**
    (Blake/Parry)
    Novello & Company Limited

21. **HUM, HUM!**
    (Barratt)
    Chester Music Limited.

22. **KOOKABURRA SITS IN THE OLD GUM TREE**
    (Sinclair)
    Campbell Connelly & Company Limited.

23. **KING WITHOUT A THING (from 'Manger Tom')**
    (Allain-Chapman/Allain)
    Novello & Company Limited

24. **LAND OF MY FATHERS (Hen Wlad Fy Nhadau)**
    (James/James)
    Novello & Company Limited

25. **LEAN ON ME**
    (Withers)
    Universal/MCA Music Limited.

CD2
OM43252

1. **LONDON BRIDGE**
   (Traditional)
   Novello & Company Limited

2. **MY GRANDFATHER'S CLOCK**
   (Work)
   Novello & Company Limited

3. **NELLIE THE ELEPHANT**
   (Butler/Hart)
   Dash Music Company Limited.

4. **PLEASE MR ORGAN-MAN**
   (Lines/Roe)
   Novello & Company Limited

5. **ON ILKLEY MOOR BAHT 'AT**
   (Traditional)
   Novello & Company Limited

6. **ORANGES AND LEMONS**
   (Sharp)
   Novello & Company Limited

7. **REACH**
   (Dennis/Todd)
   EMI Music Publishing Limited/
   Universal Music Publishing MGB Limited.

8. **RAINDROPS KEEP FALLING ON MY HEAD**
   (David/Bacharach)
   Universal/MCA Music Limited/Windswept
   Music (London) Limited/Warner/
   Chappell Music Limited.

9. **RIGHT SAID FRED**
   (Rudge/Dicks)
   Noel Gay Music Company Limited.

10. **SHOUT FOR HAPPINESS**
    (Hart/Blight)
    Campbell Connelly & Company Limited.

11. **SHOW ME THE WAY TO GO HOME**
    (King/Swain)
    Campbell Connelly & Company Limited.

12. **THE SUN HAS GOT HIS HAT ON**
    (Butler/Gay)
    EMI Music Publishing Limited/
    Richard Armitage Limited.

13. **THE SALLEY GARDENS**
    (Traditional/Yeats)
    Novello & Company Limited

14. **SCARBOROUGH FAIR**
    (Traditional)
    Novello & Company Limited

15. **THE SKYE BOAT SONG**
    (Traditional)
    Novello & Company Limited

16. **SUR LE PONT D'AVIGNON**
    (Traditional)
    Novello & Company Limited

17. **THREE LITTLE FISHES**
    (Dowell)
    Campbell Connelly & Company Limited.

18. **TOP OF THE WORLD**
    (Bettis/Carpenter) .
    Universal Music Publishing Limited.

19. **WHEN YOU BELIEVE (from The Prince Of Egypt)**
    (Schwartz)
    © Copyright 1997 DWA Songs (ASCAP).
    Cherry Lane Music Limited.

20. **WHO'S BEEN POLISHING THE SUN**
    (Gay)
    Richard Armitage Limited.

21. **WITH A LITTLE HELP FROM MY FRIENDS**
    (Lennon/McCartney)
    Sony/ATV Music Publishing (UK) Limited

22. **YE BANKS AND BRAES**
    (Traditional)
    Novello & Company Limited

23. **YOU ARE MY SUNSHINE**
    (Davis/Mitchell)
    Peermusic (UK) Limited.

24. **THIS BEAUTIFUL DAY**
    (Workman)
    Noel Gay Music Company Limited.